Let's Go
and Say Hello

Matador
9 Priory Business Park,
Wistow Road, Kibworth Beauchamp,
Leicestershire. LE8 0RX
Tel: 0116 279 2299
Email: books@troubador.co.uk
Web: www.troubador.co.uk/matador
Twitter: @matadorbooks

ISBN 978 1789017 212

British Library Cataloguing in Publication Data.
A catalogue record for this book is available from the British Library.

Matador is an imprint of Troubador Publishing Ltd

Let's Go and Say Hello
For Erykah

My name is Erica,
Born in the UK.
I heard about different countries
and said, "No way!"
Who could live there?
What could there be?
Please Mummy, let's go and see.

We first took a trip to Spain,
Unlike home it did hardly rain.
Spanish were the words I could hear,
To say "Hola" I had no fear.
I met a friend called José,
Together we had so much fun and play.

Paella for dinner,
Flamenco is the dance.
Time to say "Goodbye,"
Next destination: France.

Going up the Eiffel Tower,
Felt like the finest hour.
French were the words I could hear,
To say "Bonjour" I had no fear.
I say "Yes," Maria says "Oui"
What great friends we came to be.

"Ooh-la-la" and "Au revoir"
Are words in French I now know.
Time to say "Goodbye,"
Next stop: Tokyo.

Tokyo is in Japan,
Noodles cooking in a big pan.
Japanese were the words I could hear,
To say "Konnichiwa" I had no fear.
Yuna is my Japanese friend,
Who I adore to the end.

Terriyaki for dinner,
Origami for play.
Time to say "Goodbye,"
To China without delay.

One of the biggest countries of all,
China has a very famous long wall.
Mandarin were the words I could hear,
To say "Ni Hao" I had no fear.
My Chinese friend is called Wen,
Together we built a big den.

Lanterns, fans
And feng shui.
Now to India
Mummy takes me.

Upon arrival in Mumbai,
We gave hot curry a try.
Hindi were the words I could hear,
To say "Namaste" I had no fear.
I met a friend called Riyen,
He taught me to count in Hindi to ten.

Colours, spices
And the Taj Mahal.
Go to South America?
Yes, we shall.

Upon landing in Brazil,
The carnival gave us such a thrill.
Portuguese were the words
I could hear,
To say "Oi" I had no fear.
I made a friend called Gael,
So much fun to tell a tale.

Samba in Rio,
Below a statue.
On to Africa
We then flew.

Elephants call Kenya home,
Where leopards and lions freely roam.
Swahili were the words I could hear,
To say "Jambo" I had no fear.
With Isaac we had so much fun,
Playing drums under the African sun.

Mountains, safari,
And a beautiful lake.
Now a trip home,
I must take.

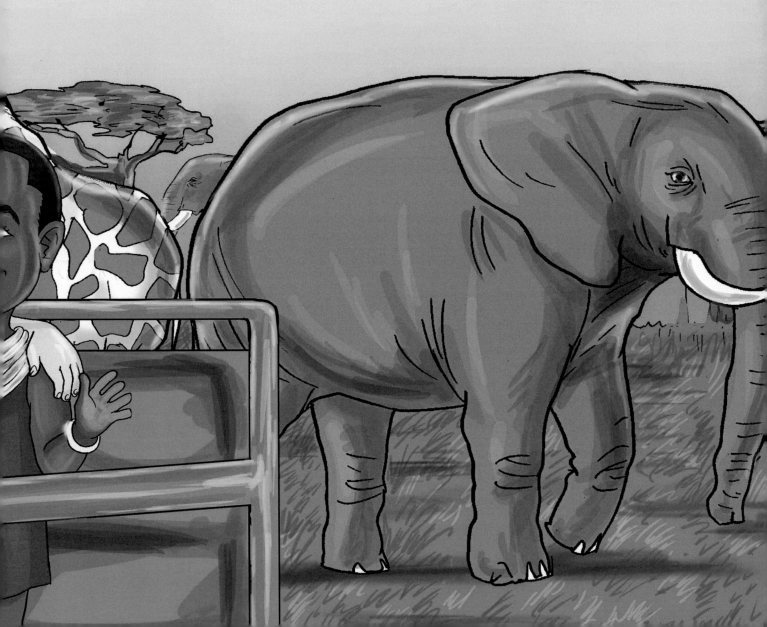

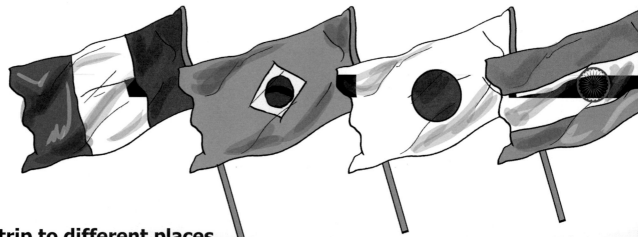

On my trip to different places,
I met friends of all races.
Different colours
Different faces.

Whatever your colour
Or your creed,
We are all human
Of the same breed.

Now I must
Thank my Mum.

On our trip
We had so much fun

I learnt to love my friends of all races,
Of different colours with different faces.

Not knowing them would be such a shame,
We may look different but we are all the same.

Mummy tells me there are
more countries to see.
Who could live there?
What could there be?
Please Mummy, let us go.
Let's go and say "Hello!"

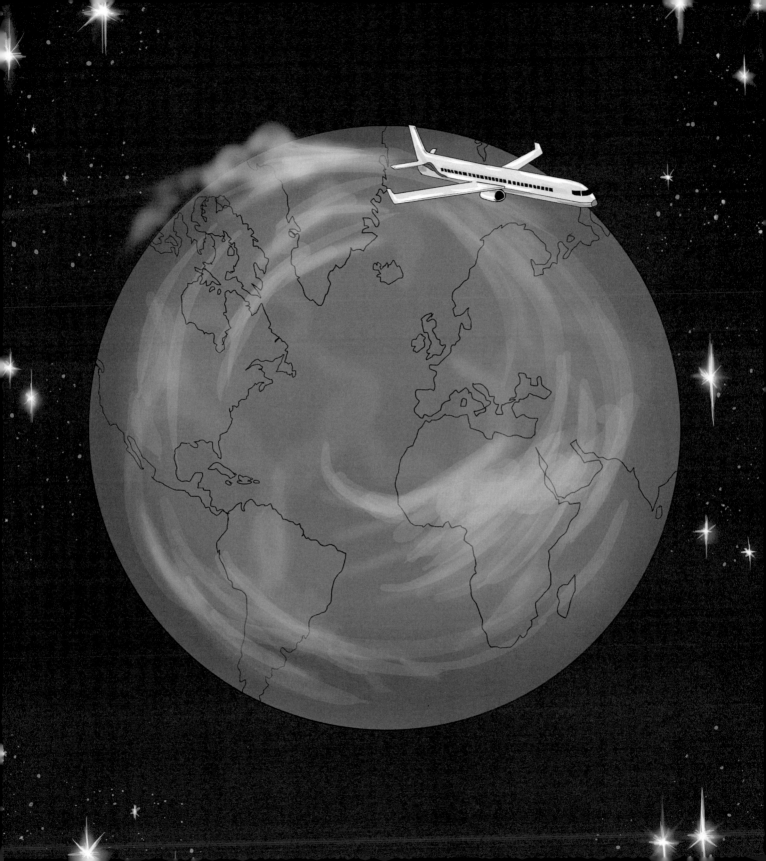

Enjoy your Journey

We would love to hear from you. We would love to see photos of your reading the book, or with your friends, or on your travels.

Facebook: Let's Go and Say Hello
Twitter: @letsgosayhello
Instagram: letsgoandsayhello